WORDS THEIR WAY®

WORD STUDY IN ACTION • WITHIN WORD PATTERN

Glenview, Illinois

Boston, Massachusetts

Chandler, Arizona

Upper Saddle River, New Jersey

ALWAYS LEARNING

PEARSON

Photographs

Every effort has been made to secure permission and provide appropriate credit for photographic material. The publisher deeply regrets any omission and pledges to correct errors called to its attention in subsequent editions.

Unless otherwise acknowledged, all photographs are the property of Pearson Education, Inc.

Photo locators denoted as follows: Top (T), Center (C), Bottom (B), Left (L), Right (R), Background (Bkgd)

Cover ©Coyote-Photography/Alamy Images; **1** (Plate) ©Artur Synenko/Shutterstock, (Hat) ©Heath Doman/Shutterstock, (Game) ©Tatik22/Shutterstock, (Frame) ©Valentin Agapov/Shutterstock, (Map) Digital Wisdom, Inc., (Snake, Crab, Bat) Getty Images, (Grass) Stockdisc; **9** (Pig) ©Anat-oli/Shutterstock, (Kite) ©D. Hurst/Alamy, (Fish) ©Eric Isselée/Shutterstock, (Pie) Brand X Pictures/Thinkstock, (Prize) Comstock/Thinkstock, (Hive) Corbis/Jupiter Images, (Swim, Fire) Getty Images, (Twins) John Foxx/Thinkstock, (Hill, Dive) Photos to Go/Photolibrary, (Bride) Thinkstock; **11** (Pig) ©Anat-oli/Shutterstock, (Kite) ©D. Hurst/Alamy; **12** (Pig) ©Anat-oli/Shutterstock, (Kite) ©D. Hurst/Alamy; **13** (Pig) ©Anat-oli/Shutterstock, (Kite) ©D. Hurst/Alamy; **15** (Pig) ©Anat-oli/Shutterstock, (Kite) ©D. Hurst/Alamy; **16** (Pig) ©Anat-oli/Shutterstock, (Kite) ©D. Hurst/Alamy; **17** (Road) ©Alexey Stiop/Shutterstock, (Goat) ©Eric Isselée/Shutterstock, (Fox) ©Jeremy Woodhouse/Getty Images, (Boat) ©ThinkStock/SuperStock, (Mop) Stockbyte/Thinkstock; **25** (Walnut) ©M. Unal Ozmen/Shutterstock, (Bug) Brand X Pictures/Thinkstock, (Trunk, Flute, Mule) Getty Images, (Moon) Thinkstock; **33** (Tree) ©Borislav Gnjidic/Shutterstock, (Sleep) ©Corbis Super RF/Alamy, (Leaf) ©Royalty-Free/Corbis, (Sheep) Getty Images, (Seal) ImageShop/Jupiter Images, (Nest, Bell) Jupiter Images, (Queen) Stockbyte/Thinkstock, (Jeep) Photos to Go/Photolibrary.

ISBN-13: 978-1-4284-3133-1
ISBN-10:   1-4284-3133-0

15 16 V011 17 16 15

Contents

ă		Oddball
ā		

Write two short *a* vowel words and two long *a* vowel words on the lines. Then draw a picture to match each word.

ă cat

ā cake

Sort 1: Short and Long a (Pictures)

Oddball					

ī					

ĭ					

Write two short i vowel words and two long i vowel words on the lines. Then draw a picture to match each word.

ĭ   pig

ī   kite

Sort 3: Short and Long i (Pictures)

Sort 5

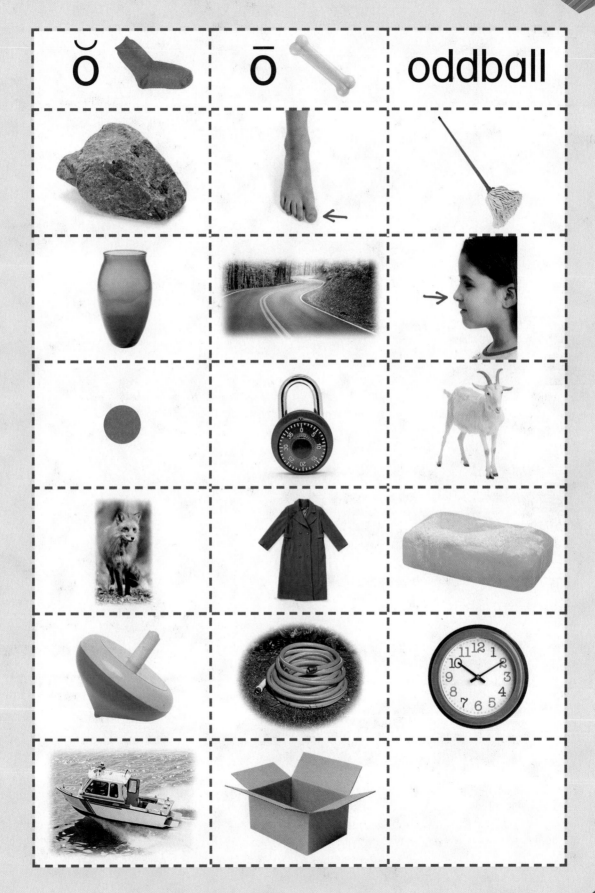

Short and Long o (Pictures)

Oddball			

ō

o

Write two short *o* vowel words and two long *o* vowel words on the lines. Then draw a picture to match each word.

Ŏ 🧦 sock	Ō 🦴 bone

Sort 5: Short and Long o (Pictures)

Short and Long u (Pictures)

Oddball					

ū

ŭ

Write two short u vowel words and two long u vowel words on the lines. Then draw a picture to match each word.

Ŭ cup

Ū tube

Sort 7: Short and Long u (Pictures)

ĕ	ē	oddball

Oddball			

ē

e

Write two short e vowel words and two long e vowel words on the lines. Then draw a picture to match each word.

ĕ bed	ē feet

CVC-short	CVCe-long	oddball
crop	**note**	
mule	done	wax
rule	skin	safe
crab	wife	lots
cape	tide	gum
have	drip	vote
which	wipe	

Oddball			

CVCe-long			
note			

CVC-short			
crop			

Say each word. Decide if the word is a short vowel or long vowel word. Write the word on the lines in the box that match the vowel type.

which	drip	note	wax
safe	gum	crop	rule
wipe	vote	mule	skin

CVC-short	CVCe-long
crop	note

brain	dash	mane
faint	camp	train
stamp	blame	paint
said	snake	crane
snack	want	main
flash	place	snail
bake	black	

ă CVC	ā CVCe	ā CVVC-ai	Oddball
cat	face	rain	

Say each short a and long a word. Write on the lines words from the box that have each vowel sound and pattern.

brain	mane	camp	train	dash	faint
snake	snail	paint	crane	place	blame
flash	black	main	snack	bake	stamp

ă cat	ā face	ā rain

clock	note	stone
none	crop	chose
whole	cross	slope
boat	joke	float
coat	love	shop
lock	toast	soap
knock	toad	

Short o (CVC) and Long o (CVCe and CVVC-oa)

ŏ CVC	ō CVCe	ō CVVC	Oddball
lost	drove	road	

Say each short o and long o word. Write on the lines words from the box that have each vowel sound and pattern.

clock	stone	soap	slope	cross	note
float	whole	crop	toad	chose	toast
shop	lock	joke	knock	coat	boat

Ŏ lost	Ō road	Ō drove

Short o (CVC) and Long o
(CVCe, CVVC-oa, and CVV-ow)

drop	wrote	roam	slow	long
shop	globe	boat	roast	blow
note	throw	know	gloss	loaf
close	chop	grow	lose	dome
				coach

Short o (CVC) and Long o (CVCe, CVVC-oa, and CVV-ow)

Ŏ CVC	Ō CVCe	ŌA CVVC	ŌW CVV	Oddball
stock	froze	coal	show	

Sort 14: Short o (CVC) and Long o (CVCe, CVVC-oa, and CVV-ow)   (55)

ŏ CVC	ō CVCe	ōā CVVC	ōw CVV
stock	**froze**	**coal**	**show**

coach   drop   dome   shop
blow   roast   throw   chop
loaf   grow   wrote   globe

prune	cute	bloom
bump	flute	skunk
tooth	build	trust
grunt	bruise	smooth
built	plus	juice
crude	spoon	mule
suit	cruise	moon

Short u (CVC) and Long u (CVCe and CVVC)

Ŭ CVC	Ū CVCe	Ūi CVVC	ŌŌ CVVC	Oddball
crust	cube	fruit	food	

Say each short u and long u word. Write on the lines words from the box that have each vowel sound.

mule	bloom	cute	cruise
flute	skunk	tooth	trust
suit	grunt	juice	moon

Ŭ crust

_____
_____
_____

Ū cube

_____
_____
_____

Uı̄ fruit

_____
_____
_____

ŌŌ food

_____
_____
_____

keep	sweep	vest
next	jeep	team
leaf	when	teeth
sleep	week	heat
west	wheat	been
clean	web	weak
dress		

Short e (CVC) and Long e (CVVC)

ĕ CVC	ēe CVVC	ēa CVVC	Oddball
less	feet	mean	

Say each short e and long e word. Write on the lines words from the box that have each vowel sound and pattern.

sweep	vest	team	clean	web	heat
next	teeth	west	sleep	keep	dress
when	wheat	jeep	leaf	weak	week

ĕ less	ē̄e feet	ēa mean

reach	street	head
queen	great	steam
bread	sweet	bead
dream	thread	best
beach	desk	greed
web	breath	sleep
next	sled	threat

More Short e (CVC and CVVC) and Long e (CVVC)

ĕ CVC	ĕa CVVC	ēe CVVC	ēa CVVC	Oddball
when	dead	trees	each	

Say each short e and long e word. Write on the lines words from the box that have each vowel sound.

head	queen	best	bead
desk	dream	street	bread
sleep	reach	next	threat

ĕ when

_____

ĕa dead

_____

ēe trees

_____

ēa each

_____

Review CVVC Patterns ai, oa, ee, ea

wait	beet	beast	throat
pail	need	cream	beach
train	sheep	coat	coast
wheel	grain	goat	seat
toast	tail	three	neat
road	cheat	cheek	bait

ēā						

ēē						

ōā						

ī ī						

Sort 20: Review CVVC Patterns ai, oa, ee, ea

(79)

ai	oa	ee	ea

Sort 20: Review CVVC Patterns ai, oa, ee, ea

sigh	bliss	night
try	twice	quit
bright	white	dry
fight	cry	whisk
grill	grim	quite
high	shy	rise
grime	sky	

ĭ CVC	ī CVCe	ī igh VCC	ȳ y=ī CV
quick	write	might	why

Say each short i and long i word. Write on the lines words from
the box that have each vowel pattern.

dry	sigh	bliss
bright	white	night
	cry	try
	whisk	grime
		fight
		sky
		quite
		grill
		quit
		twice

ĭ CVC	ī CVCe	ī igh VCC	y=ī CV
quick	**write**	**might**	**why**

Sort 21: Short i (CVC) and Long i (CVCe, VCC-igh, and CV Open Syllable-y)

ī CVCe	ī igh VCC	y=ī CV	ī iCC	oddball
side	**fight**	**sky**	**wild**	
blind	mind	spy	might	guy
sign	flight	child	write	why
sight	fry	spice	nice	kind
right	stripe	fly	mice	my

ī CVCe	ī igh VCC	y=ī CV	ī iCC	Oddball
side	fight	sky	wild	

Say each long vowel word. Write the word in the box that shows the vowel sound.

| blind | write | stripe | right | why | flight | mice | mind |
| might | spy | my | child | nice | kind | fly | sight |

ī CVCe	ī̄ igh VCC	y=ī CV	ī iCC
side	**fight**	**sky**	**wild**

r-Influenced Vowel Patterns ar, ir, or, ur

start	burn	first	fork
horn	harm	hurt	dirt
curl	birth	north	sharp
corn	dark	swirl	burst
stir	surf	storm	harp
porch	girl	curb	shark

ur						
turn						

or						
form						

ir						
bird						

ar						
part						

Sort 23: r-Influenced Vowel Patterns ar, ir, or, ur

(91)

Write on the lines words from your sort with the same r-influenced vowel pattern as part, bird, form, and turn.

part	bird	form	turn

r-Influenced Vowel Patterns ar, are, air

dark	bear	stair	fare
heart	chair	square	start
harm	bare	lair	sharp
pear	fair	pair	stare
wear	hare	shark	where

Oddball	air	are	ar
	hair	care	part

Say each word aloud. Write on the line a word that sounds the same but is spelled differently and has a different meaning. Then draw a picture of the word you wrote.

pair	stare	bare
_____	_____	_____

fare	where	hare
_____	_____	_____

Sort 24: r-Influenced Vowel Patterns ar, are, air

r-Influenced Vowel Patterns er, ear, eer

er	ear	eer	ear = ur
her	ear	deer	earn
perch	fear	steer	earth
herd	clear	dear	cheer
heard	peer	fern	year
near	learn	germ	clerk

Sort 25: r-Influenced Vowel Patterns er, ear, eer   (97)

er	ear	eer	ear = ur
her	ear	deer	earn

Write on the lines words from your sort with the same vowel sound and pattern as her, ear, deer, and earn.

her	ear	deer	earn

r-Influenced Vowel Patterns ir, ire, ier

ir	ire	ier	oddball
bird	**fire**	**drier**	
third	girl	birth	tire
flier	shirt	fir	their
hire	pliers	crier	wire
frier	fur		

r-Influenced Vowel Patterns ir, ire, ier

ir	ire	ier	Oddball
bird	**fire**	**drier**	

Write on the lines words from your sort with the same vowel sound and pattern as bird, fire, and drier.

bird	fire	drier

r-Influenced Vowel Patterns or, ore, oar

soar	work	horse	more	store
sore	worse	roar	for	wore
four	floor	tore	storm	boar
corn	world	worm	hoarse	fork
			oar	poor

r-Influenced Vowel Patterns or, ore, oar

or	ore	oar	w + or	Oddball
form	shore	board	word	

Sort 27: r-Influenced Vowel Patterns or, ore, oar   (107)

Write on the lines words from your sort with the same vowel sound and pattern as form, shore, board, and word.

form	shore	board	word

Sort 27: r-Influenced Vowel Patterns or, ore, oar

Sort
28

ur	ure	ur-e	oddball
turn	**sure**	**curve**	
pure	burn	hurt	curl
surf	lure	nurse	cure
purse	burst	churn	curse
hurl	blur	church	curb

r-Influenced Vowel Patterns ur, ure, ur-e

ur-e					
curve					

ure					
sure					

ur					
turn					

Write on the lines words from your sort with the same vowel sound and pattern as turn, sure, and curve.

turn	sure	curve

torn	hard	score
earn	snore	nerve
snort	worth	card
bore	yard	spur
horse	search	jar
chore	bar	sharp
pearl	march	worst

ar	ər	or

| hard | score | earn | snore | nerve | pearl | worth | card | bore |
| yard | spur | horse | search | jar | chore | bar | sharp | torn |

ar	er	or

oi	oy	
point	**boy**	broil
join	soil	soy
spoil	oil	coil
joy	coin	moist
joint	boil	toy

oy					
boy					

oi					
point					

Write each word on a line.
Choose beginning and ending letters to make words with *oi* or *oy*.

p	s	b	c	j	t	n	l	sp	nt

oi

oy

Sort 30: Diphthongs oi, oy

Vowel Digraph oo

would	spoon	nook	fool
stool	could	hook	brook
crook	troop	root	hood
spool	wood	hoop	noon
groom	foot	tool	should
	soot	wool	stood

Vowel Digraph oo

$\overline{OO} = \overline{U}$
soon

$\breve{OO}$
good

Oddball

c f h st r l n k d t p

oō = ū   oŏ

ground	south	mouth	pound
couch	frown	town	clown
drown	owl	howl	tough
plow	shout	growl	count
gown	scout	cloud	crown
	rough	found	grown

OU		OW		Oddball
sound		**brown**		

t h n l s cl c b r f sc d g p

ou

ow

aw	au	oddball
saw	**caught**	
lawn	cause	paw
straw	fault	law
claw	sauce	taught
draw	laugh	haul
pause	yawn	haunt
hawk	crawl	dawn
launch	vault	

	aw	au	Oddball
	saw	**caught**	

Choose beginning and ending letters to make words with *aw* or *au*. Write each word on a line.

s p l c d r h m e t v f n g y

aw	au

wa	al	ou
watch	**small**	**thought**
walk	salt	wash
tall	bought	wand
almost	wasp	fought
swap	chalk	ought
swat	brought	cough
also		

wa	al	ou
watch	**small**	**thought**

| wash | almost | wand | small | brought | cough | thought | talk |
| bought | walk | ought | wasp | watch | also | tall | swap |

wa

al

ou

-ck short	-ke long	-k other
kick	**take**	**took**
bike	sick	lock
shook	shake	duck
duke	spoke	pack
strike	cook	lick
sock	smoke	look
truck	like	book

-k other								
took								

-ke long								
take								

-ck short								
kick								

-ck short	-ke long	-k other

Silent Beginning Consonants kn-, wr-, gn-

kn-	wr-	gn-	oddball
knife	**wrong**	**gnat**	
rap	knack	wreck	known
wrist	knot	gnaw	ring
wrap	knob	knit	wren
wring	knight	knoll	write
wreath	night	not	

kn-	wr-	gn-	Oddball
kinfe	wrong	gnat	

Write on the lines words from your sort that begin with kn-, wr-, and gn-.

kn-
knife

wr-
wrong

gn-
gnat

throne	squirm	threw
shrink	shrub	shrug
squint	shriek	squeak
squeeze	threat	squish
squash	shrunk	throw
shrewd	thrill	shrimp
through	squawk	thrifty

squ-
square

shr-
shred

thr-
three

Write on the lines words from your sort that begin with thr-, shr-, and squ-.

thr-	shr-	squ-

scr-	str-	spr-
screen	**strong**	**spring**
stress	scrap	strict
straight	scream	string
scrape	spray	spruce
strange	scratch	stripe
stretch	sprout	scram
scribe	spread	script

spr- spring							

str- strong							

scr- screen							

Write on the lines words from your sort that begin
with scr-, str-, and spr-.

scr-	str-	spr-

Sort 38: Triple r-Blends scr-, str-, spr-

germ	cub	gym	coat
cent	corn	gem	cease
game	calf	guide	guess
goose	cart	cell	guest
	gist	golf	code

Hard and Soft c and g

soft c	hard c	soft g	hard g
city	card	giant	gave

| cell | goose | gist | coat | calf | gym | cub | guest |
| golf | code | gem | cease | game | cent | guide | cart |

hard c	soft c	hard g	soft g

badge	charge	stage
rage	ridge	surge
range	judge	cage
huge	fudge	change
dodge	page	sponge
bridge	bulge	

Sort 40: Word Endings -dge, -ge

-dge	-ge	r,l,n+ -ge
edge	age	large

Write on the lines words from your sort that end in -dge or -ge.

-dge	-ge

-ce	-ve	-se
chance	**move**	**please**
prince	tease	leave
glove	choose	dance
fence	shove	piece
cheese	peace	wise
solve	bounce	prove
raise	glance	twelve

-se							
please							

-ve							
move							

-ce							
chance							

Choose beginning and middle letters to make words with ending letters -ce, -ve, and -se. Write each word on a line.

| ch | pr | p | b | gl | l | s | t | pl | o | an | in | en | ea | oo | ee | ie |

-ce	-ve	-se

witch	torch	peach
screech	gulch	pitch
coach	bench	sketch
which	fetch	branch
beach	rich	match
speech	much	crunch
hutch	teach	munch

-tch	-ch	r,l,n+ -ch	Oddball
catch	reach	porch	

Write on the lines words from your sort that end with -tch or -ch.

-tch	-ch

stake	tale
fair	wail
wait	mane
bail	stair
made	hair
plane	main
bale	tail
bear	hare
plain	steak
bare	fare
maid	stare
whale	weight

Say each word aloud. Write on the line a word that sounds the same but is spelled differently and has a different meaning. Then write a sentence that uses the new word.

tale _____

stake _____

fare _____

whale _____

wait _____

main _____

stair _____

maid _____

hare _____

plain _____

bare _____

bale _____

rein	sale
waist	break
rain	ate
pale	pair
pain	rays
pear	vein
eight	weigh
pail	vain
pane	vane
waste	sail
raise	way
brake	pare

Say each word aloud. Write on the line a word that sounds the same but is spelled differently and has a different meaning. Then write a sentence that uses the new word.

rein _____

sail _____

waist _____

brake _____

weigh _____

daze _____

pane _____

vein _____

pare _____

rays _____

pale _____

ate _____

mist	in
dye	it's
missed	I
night	billed
fined	eye
write	him
side	hi
its	sighed
build	knight
die	find
right	inn
high	hymn

Say each word aloud. Write on the line a word that sounds the same but is spelled differently and has a different meaning. Then write a sentence that uses the new word.

missed _____

inn _____

die _____

its _____

eye _____

night _____

billed _____

fined _____

right _____

hymn _____

side _____

hi _____